CONTENTS

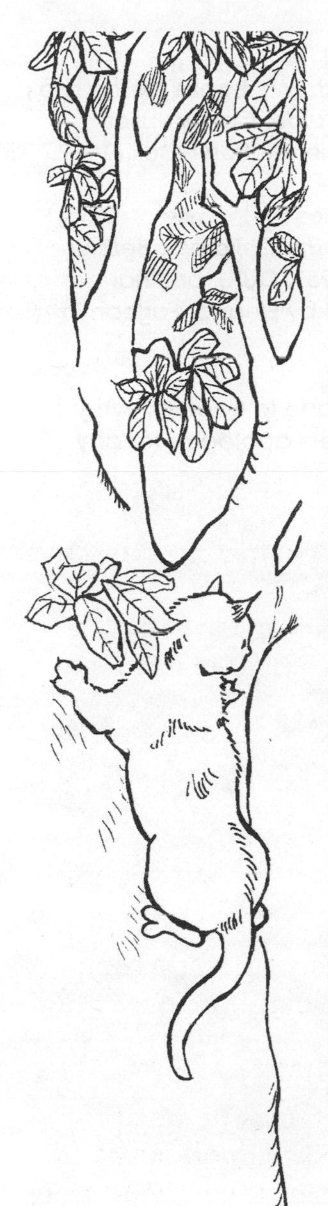
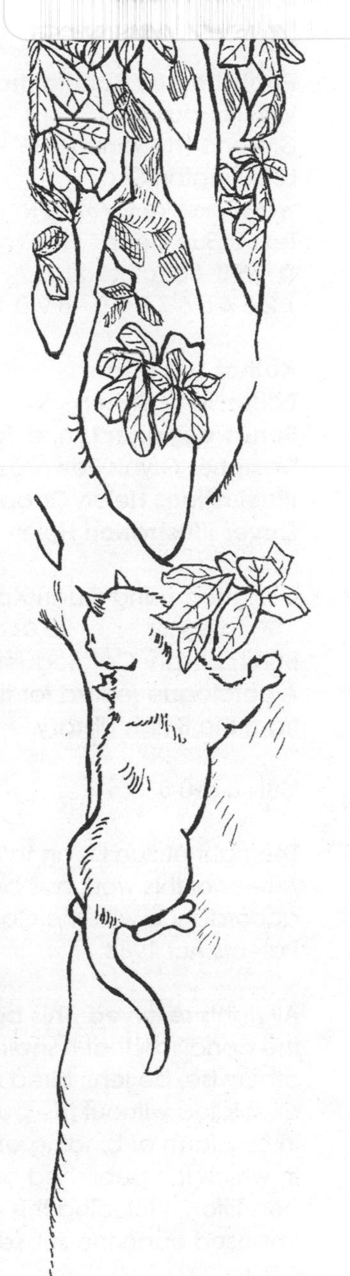

The House Cat
by Helen Cooper

INTRODUCTION

CREDITS
Published by Scholastic Ltd,
Villiers House,
Clarendon Avenue,
Leamington Spa,
Warwickshire CV32 5PR
Text © Sue Dean
© 1998 Scholastic Ltd
1 2 3 4 5 6 7 8 9 0 8 9 0 1 2 3 4 5 6 7

Author Sue Dean
Editor Jane Bishop
Series designer Lynne Joesbury
Designer Glynis Edwards
Illustrations Helen Cooper
Cover illustration Helen Cooper

Designed using QuarkXpress

British Library Cataloguing-in-Publication Data
A catalogue record for this book is available from the British Library.

ISBN 0-590-53859-4

ACKNOWLEDGEMENTS
Dorling Kindersley Children's Books for the use of text from *Eyewitness Guide: Cat* by Juliet Clutton-Brock © 1992, Juliet Clutton-Brock (1992, Dorling Kindersley).
David Higham Associates for the use of 'Cats' by Eleanor Farjeon from *The Children's Bells* © 1957, Eleanor Farjeon (1957, OUP), original copyright 1938, renewed by Eleanor Farjeon in 1966.

Every effort has been made to trace copyright holders and the publishers apologize for any inadvertent omissions.

INTRODUCTION

The House Cat
by Helen Cooper

WHAT'S THE PLOT OF THE STORY?

The House Cat tells the story of Tom-Cat, who lives 'in all the house'. When his owners move to another house, Tom-Cat decides that he wants to go back to **his** house where he was the House-Cat. He has lots of adventures before he finally reaches home and becomes the House-Cat once again.

WHAT'S SO GOOD ABOUT THIS BOOK?

This seems like a simple picture book, but there's more to it than that. It raises all kinds of questions such as 'Who really owns this cat?', 'Will he manage to get back to his house?' and 'What will happen when he gets there?' The beautiful pictures add to our understanding of the story and the characters. It has a strong message for all pet owners to think about.

ABOUT HELEN COOPER

Helen Cooper was born in 1963 and always wanted to write and draw. She trained as a music teacher, then decided that teaching was not for her. So she wrote and illustrated a book called *Kit and the Magic Kite*. Since then she has written lots of picture books and really enjoys her job. She often gets ideas for new stories when she is in the bath or on a journey somewhere. Her advice to young writers and illustrators is to never give up because you think you are not good enough. Keep trying, and you may become good enough.

Picture clues

● Look carefully at these two pictures which come before the story starts. They tell us some interesting things about the story before we read it.

● With a partner, talk about these questions:
What sort of house is this? Who might live here? What is the cat like?

● Jot down your ideas around the pictures.

Who do you think is the main character in the story?

____

What other people might be in the story?

____

Picture flicking

In picture books, words and pictures work together to tell the story. You find out some important things from the words and other important things from the pictures.

Here are four pictures from *The House Cat*.

- Working with a partner, use the pictures to tell a story.

- Talk to your partner about the pictures and how each one tells a part of the story.

- Tell each other your story and remember it. Write it down if you need to. You will be able to check it against Helen Cooper's story when you have read the book.

WAYS IN

Cat poems

- Read these poems about cats.

Catalogue

Cats sleep fat and walk thin,
Cats, when they sleep, slump;
When they wake, pull in –
And where the plump's been
There's skin.
Cats walk thin.

Cats wait in a lump,
Jump in a streak.
Cats, when they jump, are sleek
As a grape slipping its skin –
They have technique.
Oh, cats don't creak.
They sneak.

Cats sleep fat.
They spread comfort beneath them
Like a good mat,
As if they picked the place
And then sat.
You walk around one
As if he were the City Hall
After that.

Rosalie Moore

Cats

Cats sleep
Anywhere,
Any table,
Any chair,
Top of piano,
Window-ledge,
In the middle,
On the edge,
Open drawer,
Empty shoe,
Anybody's
Lap will do,
Fitted in a
Cardboard box,
In the cupboard
With your
frocks –
Anywhere!
They don't care!
Cats sleep
Anywhere.

Eleanor Farjeon

Cat poems (cont.)

What do you think Rosalie Moore likes about cats?

___

What do you think Eleanor Farjeon likes about cats?

___

Which poem would fit into which shape?

- Underline in red the rhymes in 'Cats'. What pattern do you notice?
- Underline in blue the rhymes in 'Catalogue'. What pattern do you notice?

What differences do you notice between the rhyme patterns in the two poems?

___

Do the poems remind you of a cat you know or have read about?

___

- Talk about the poems with a partner.

House-Cat eyes

- Read the first two pages of the story and look closely at the pictures.

- Write down what you learn from the words.

___

___

- Write down what you learn from the pictures.

___

___

Some people believe that people's eyes show what they are really like.
What does the picture of the house in Tom-Cat's eyes tell you about him?

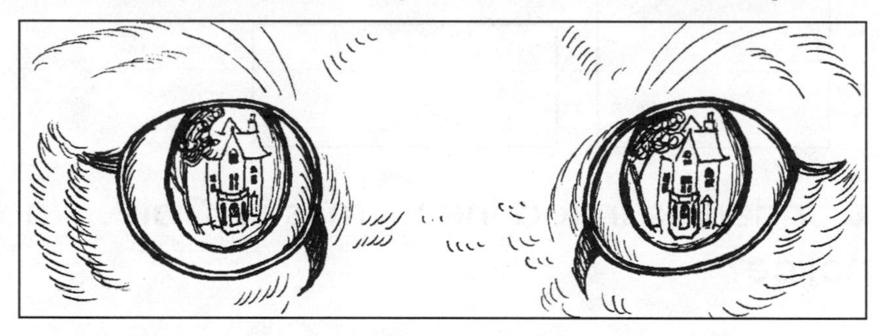

- Choose another creature – it could be a pet or a wild animal – and think of what picture (or symbol) you might find in that creature's eyes. Draw it here.

- Swap pictures with a partner and tell each other what you think the picture or symbol in its eyes tells you about the creature.

Building character

● Read the next four pages, up to where Tom-Cat purrs, "for I am the House-Cat."

Helen Cooper uses words and pictures to tell us about the people in the house.

The Spode-Fawcetts think that Tom-Cat belongs to them.

● Re-read the page about the Spode-Fawcetts. Choose three words or phrases that tell you Helen Cooper wants you not to like them very much.

____

____

● Now look at the illustrations on that page. What do they tell us about the Spode-Fawcetts?

____

____

● Turn the page and read about Jennifer. Choose three words or phrases that tell you Helen Cooper wants you to like Jennifer.

____

____

How does the picture add to your ideas?

____

____

Creating a mood

● Read up to where the Spode-Fawcetts put Tom-Cat in a box in the boot of their car.

● Underline the words in this passage that tell you the House-Cat is really **angry**.

"I will spit and I will claw!"
growls Tom-Cat when he sees
what's going on.
But Mrs Spode-Fawcett picks
him up, and squashes him into
a cardboard cage.
"You can't do this to me!" he
rages,
"I am the House-Cat."

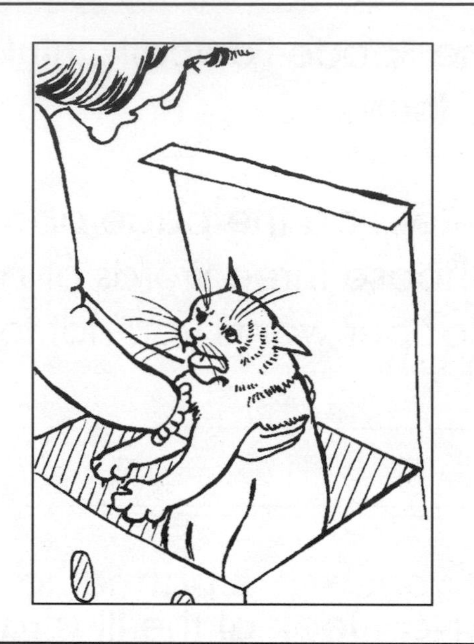

Here is the passage again. This time many of the verbs have been left out.

● Fill in the gaps with some different verbs of your own. Can you change Tom-Cat's mood? Can you make him feel upset and sad by choosing different verbs for the gaps?

"I will __________ and I will __________!" __________
Tom-Cat when he sees what's going on.
But Mrs Spode-Fawcett picks him up, and
__________ him into a cardboard cage.
"You can't do this to me!" he __________ ,
"I am the House-Cat."

Creating a mood (cont.)

● Look again at this passage.

"I will spit and I will claw!" growls Tom-Cat when he sees what's going on. But Mrs Spode-Fawcett picks him up, and squashes him into a cardboard cage.
"You can't do this to me!" he rages, "I am the House-Cat."

Helen Cooper writes the story as if it's happening now. To do this she uses the present tense. For example, 'picks him up', 'squashes him'.
Perhaps she thinks that makes the story more exciting.

● Work with a partner to fill in the gaps in the passage changing it from the present tense to the past tense.

"I will spit and I will claw!" __________ Tom-Cat when he __________ what __________ going on.
But Mrs Spode-Fawcett __________ him up, and __________ him into a cardboard cage.
"You can't do this to me!" he __________,
"I am the House-Cat!"

● With your partner, talk about which passage sounds better: the one written in the present tense, or the one in the past tense. Why do you think this?

Senses similes

● Read the pages about Tom-Cat's journey to his new house. Helen Cooper's pictures give details about what Tom-Cat smells, sees, hears, senses and knows.

To tell this part of the story, just using words, you will need to use more description in order to show with your words what Helen Cooper shows in the pictures.

For example, instead of: *the box is hard* you could write *the box is <u>as hard as nails</u>* or *the box <u>is hard like steel</u>*.

The underlined parts are similes. We use similes to compare one thing to another to help our descriptions.

● Make up some similes for the rest of Tom-Cat's journey. Use Helen Cooper's pictures to help you.

1 *his claws hurt*
his claws hurt like ______________________________

2 *he smells something good*
he smells something good, as ______________ as ______________

3 *he sees great white birds*
he sees great white birds, like ______________________________

4 *he hears a horrid noisy highway*
he hears a horrid noisy highway, as ______________________________

5 *he senses dogs*
he senses dogs, as ______________ as ______________

● Swap similes with a partner. Choose two of the best similes and draw pictures to go with them.

Tom-Cat's sense map

Cat-quick!

- Read to the end of the story.

Can you remember how Tom-Cat found his way home?
- Fill in Tom-Cat's sense map.
- Draw or write in the spaces to show what happened on his journey.
- Use your finished map to tell someone about Tom-Cat's adventures on his way home.

Jennifer is overjoyed to see Tom-Cat again. She has lots of questions about his journey. How would Tom-Cat reply to her questions?

Animal instincts

Can you remember the part where Tom-Cat decides to go home? The book says "... and somehow, in his head he knows the way."

Tom-Cat knows his way home by instinct. He uses all his senses to create a special sense map.

● Without looking back at the book, fill in the things Tom-Cat senses on his journey home.

Tom-Cat's journey home

He smells ________________

He sees ________________

He hears ________________

He senses ________________

He knows ________________

Now think about **your** journey from home to school.
What things do you sense on your journey?

● Fill in your name and write a list.

________________ **journey to school**

I smell ________________

I see ________________

I hear ________________

I sense ________________

I know ________________

● Use the information on your list to draw a sense map of your own journey, like Tom-Cat's.

Cat information

You use information books to find out facts about different subjects. Reading an information book about cats is quite different from reading a story book about cats.

- Write down three different pieces of information you would expect to find in a book called 'Caring for your Cat'.

____

____

____

- Now read these headings carefully.

Scratch clean	Creature comforts
Cat kit	Moggy menu

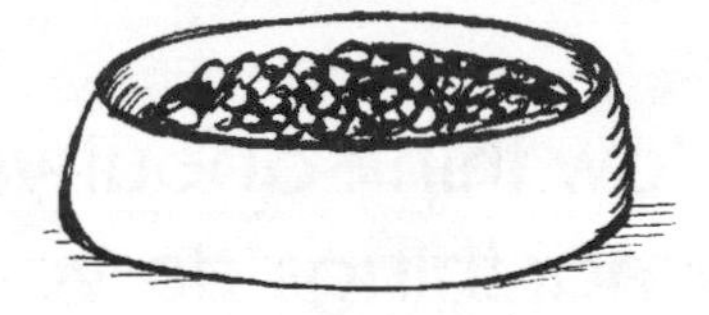

What sort of information would you expect to find under each of these headings?

- Talk with a partner first, then write your ideas here. (The first one has been started for you.)

Moggy menu – food cats like eating, such as ...

Scratch clean – ________________________________

Creature comforts – _____________________________

Cat kit – ____________________________________

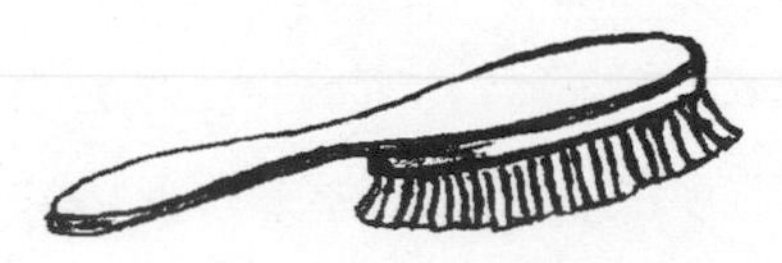

Cat information (cont.)

- Look carefully at the headings again.

Scratch clean	Creature comforts
Cat kit	Moggy menu

- Now read these paragraphs from the information book.

Cats are carnivores and need to eat meat or fish daily. Hard cat biscuits are also a good idea as they help to keep the teeth and jaws clean and healthy. Water should always be available and is essential if dried food is part of the diet. Although cats like milk it often gives them an upset stomach.

Every cat needs to clean its claws and stretch its body. An old piece of wood or mat, or a scratching post, are ideal for this.

All cats, but especially the longhaired breeds, should be brushed regularly, otherwise they swallow a lot of hair when they lick their coats. This collects in the stomach as a fur-ball, which can make the cat ill.

The cat is a territorial animal and needs its own sleeping place. However, the cat will often take over the best armchair or bed. This is probably because these places smell reassuring rather than because they are especially comfortable.

Which heading matches each of the four paragraphs?

- Write one heading above each paragraph.
- Read the paragraphs again. Now, as quickly as you can, find two pieces of equipment needed to care for a cat (underline them in red) and two things that make cats ill. (underline them in blue).

Where should Tom-Cat live?

● Imagine that when the Spode-Fawcetts find out where Tom-Cat has gone, they decide they want him back. But Jennifer says he should stay at her house. Who is in the right? You decide!

● First of all, think of reasons why the Spode-Fawcetts might want Tom-Cat back. Fill in the speech bubble.

We want Tom-Cat back because

____

____

____

Now think of reasons why Jennifer wants Tom-Cat to stay in her house.

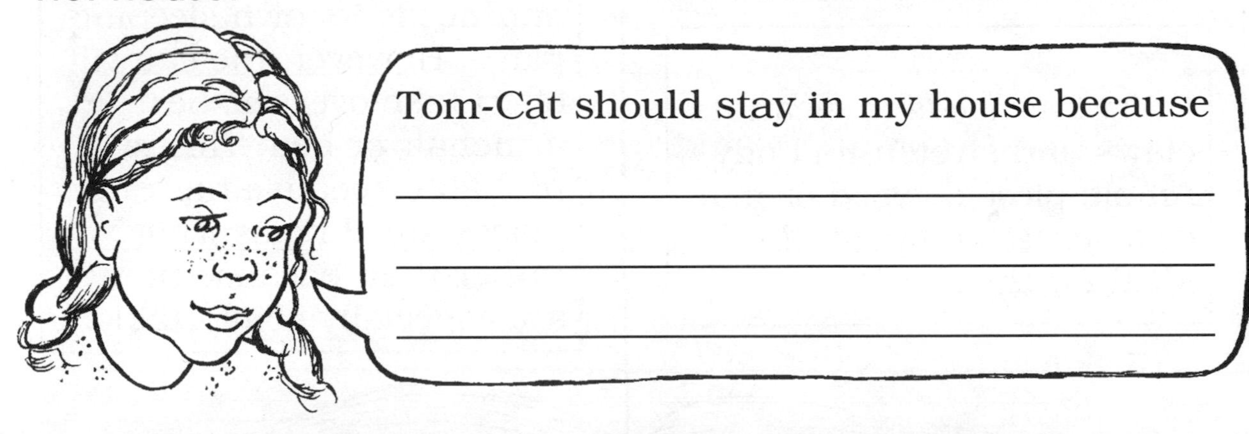

Should Tom-Cat stay with Jennifer, or go back to the Spode-Fawcetts?

● Look back through the story and find clues or evidence to support both sides. Write your ideas on a piece of paper under these headings.

'Staying with Jennifer' 'Going back to the Spode-Fawcetts'

Where should Tom-Cat live? (cont.)

Now **you** be the jury! Talk among yourselves and decide where Tom-Cat should live.

You have collected information for two sides of an argument.

● Read back over your notes and use this planner to organize an argument called: Where should Tom-Cat live?

Reasons for living with the Spode-Fawcetts	Supporting evidence

Reasons for living with Jennifer	Supporting evidence

What I think

● Check over your planner to make sure you haven't missed anything out.

● Finally, write up your argument on a separate piece of paper. If you need help, use this framework.

> I think that Tom-Cat should live with ...
> because ...
> The reasons for my thinking this are, first ...
> Another reason is ...
> Moreover ...
> I hope I have shown that ...

What makes a home?

One message in the story of *The House Cat* is that home is an important place for animals and people.

- Look back over the story (the words and the pictures) to find clues about what different characters think and feel about their home. Then fill in the chart.

	Thinks and feels about home	Evidence
Jennifer		
Mr and Mrs Spode-Fawcett		
Tom-Cat		

What does the word 'home' mean to you?

- Talk about this with a partner, then put your ideas into a stepping stone outline like this.

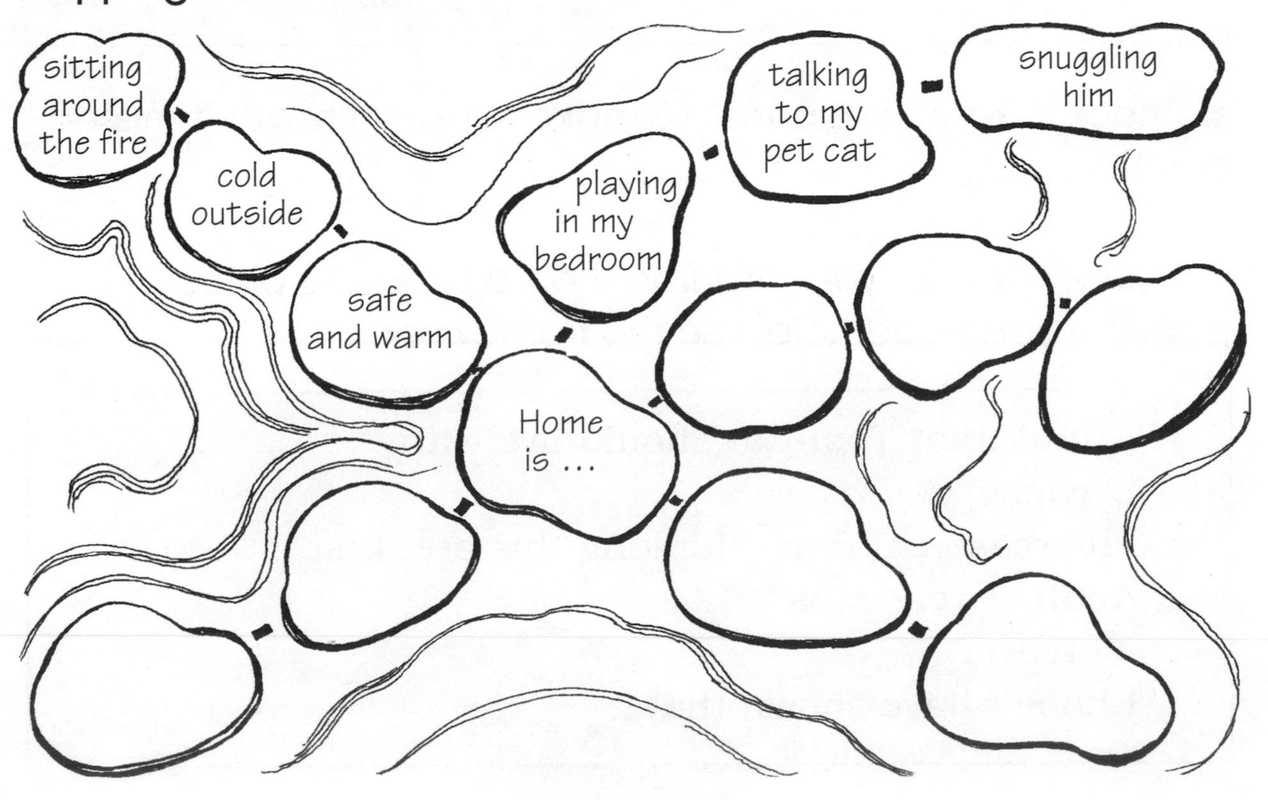

What makes a home? (cont.)

● Swap your completed stepping stones outline with a partner.

● Talk about the linked stepping stones that give you the strongest pictures in your mind.

● Write a sentence using those stones, starting with 'Home is ...'

____

● Choose another set of linked stepping stones and write another 'Home is ...' mind picture.

____

● Join up with another pair and pool your stepping stone sentences. Link them up to create a 'Home is ...' poem.

Writing a 'found' poem

A 'found' poem is when you use words or phrases from something you have read to make up a poem.
This found poem uses words and phrases about the Spode-Fawcetts:

Spode-Fawcetts
They're cross
and ungrateful
they want a pet to match
but Tom-Cat lives in all the house
House-Cat!

It is written in a special form of five lines called a cinquain.

- Count the number of syllables in each of the five lines.

first line ________ syllables

second ________ ____________

third ________ ____________

fourth ________ ____________

last line ________ ____________

What do you notice about the shape of the poem?

- Draw the outline of the poem here. Remember! Cinquain poems always have five lines and this number of syllables, and usually have this shape.

Writing a 'found' poem (cont.)

Now it's time for you to write your own cinquain poem.
- To do this, first re-read the last part of the book, from the words: "he must go quickly, no time for play ..." to the end.
- Now list all the words that you think are important in this part of the story. Two have been done for you.

no path great white birds

Remind yourself of what you found out about writing cinquains. Now use the words and phrases you have collected to write a short 'found' cinquain poem about Tom-Cat's journey home.

first line ______________________

second ______________________

third ______________________

fourth ______________________

last line ______________________

- When you have finished your poem, give it a title.

- Check: does it follow the rules for cinquains? Has it got the right number of lines and syllables? Is it the right sort of shape?

- Read it aloud to a partner. Can you improve your cinquain? Make any changes you need, then write your final version in your best handwriting.

DEVELOPING IDEAS

Cat words

Helen Cooper has made up lots of cat words to describe Tom-Cat.

House-Cat	Boat-Cat	cat-quick
cat-walk	hunting-cat	cat-raft

How many more cat words can you think of?

● Write them here and try to guess what they mean.

Cat words	What I think it means
cat flap	a cat door cut in a human door, so the cat can get in or out
cat's eye	
cat	

Some of the cat words that Helen Cooper has used are made-up words, such as cat-quick. Try to make up some new cat words of your own that would suit Tom-Cat or a cat you know.

● Write down your new word and what you want it to mean.

Cat words	What I think it means
Cat-quick	moving as quickly as a cat
cat-mat	a special mat where our cat always sleeps

Character profile

● Choose one of the characters from the story and complete this character profile sheet.

Some parts can be filled in from the story. For other parts you need to use your ideas about the character, based on what you know about them from the words and pictures.

Character profile

My name is ____________________

I was born in ____________________

I used to live ____________________

I now live ____________________

I really like ____________________

I really hate ____________________

My best friend ____________________

I wish ____________________

● Swap character profiles with a partner.

● Talk together about the things that are similar and things that are different.

A review of *The House Cat*

- Read what *Books for Keeps* said about Helen Cooper's book, *The House Cat*.

> 'Helen Cooper uses the page in exciting ways to express mood and movement and has produced a book to delight cat lovers, children and adults alike.'
> *Books For Keeps*

You will find these words printed on the back cover of the book. Do you agree or disagree with *Books for Keeps*?

- Look back through the book and think carefully.
- Use the grid to record what you think of Helen Cooper's story and illustrations. Remember to give reasons for your opinions.

Books for Keeps says	agree	disagree	My reasons are
'uses the page in exciting ways ...'			
'express mood and movement ...'			
'a book to delight cat lovers, children, and adult alike.'			

- Swap with a partner and compare your ideas.
- Write on a piece of paper a sentence saying what you think about the book, to go on the back cover of *The House Cat*.
- Follow the layout of the *Books for Keeps* words. Remember to add your own name!

USING THIS BOOK

The House Cat is a picture book that encourages children to think about why we have pets, about the nature of cats and how they relate to people and places. Helen Cooper's illustrations are lively, detailed and offer children lots of opportunities to look closely at how the story is developed not just through the words but through the pictures as well. On first reading, the story is not a complex one but the play on language, the way the characters are presented and the theme of the cat's journey do reveal hidden depths and so justifies closer study.

MANAGING THE READING OF *THE HOUSE CAT*

The three 'Ways in' activities are designed to be carried out before the children read the book.

They are there to help the children not only to focus in on and anticipate the themes of the book and the possible storyline, but also to activate their knowledge and understanding of the different ways that cats behave. The 'Making sense' and 'Developing ideas' sections are there to prompt children to look more closely at the way Helen Cooper has put the picture book together and to respond to the characters, the storyline and how language is used at both a personal and critical level.

As *The House Cat* is a short book, it should be read in its entirety to start off with and relevant activities can then be selected. It is unlikely that you would want to use all the activities with all your children as they are based on such a short book.

CLASSROOM MANAGEMENT AND SUPPORT

The House Cat can be used as a shared reading experience with the whole class over the course of a week. The children can read and re-read the story with a different focus on each occasion. You can then use the activities with smaller groups of children to explore particular moments in the story or to reinforce aspects of the writing craft as demonstrated in the story.

The Teachers' notes on pages 30–32 offer ideas for whole-class modelled reading and writing activities, to introduce a new idea or part of the reading and writing process which can then be explored more collaboratively in a small group context.

The book is a helpful support within the Literacy Hour framework, but can also be used more flexibly according to an individual teacher's preferred classroom organization. It could also be used as part of a group – guided reading session. The activities are designed so that the children get plenty of opportunities to discuss their ideas and work collaboratively.

DIFFERENTIATION IN ACTIVITIES

Although there is a planned structure in the 'Making sense' section of this book, there is no intention that the children have to do all of the activities. Indeed, in such a short picture book it would probably dampen the children's enthusiasm for the book if they had to complete all the tasks.

All of the activities are designed to be accessible to children in a mainstream primary classroom and differentiation will come from their differing levels of response.

Individual writing tasks may need to be supported by teacher modelling where appropriate. Mixed ability groups are also a useful way of providing help to support less confident readers and writers. The teachers' notes give ideas for extension activities to enable you to challenge more able readers and writers.

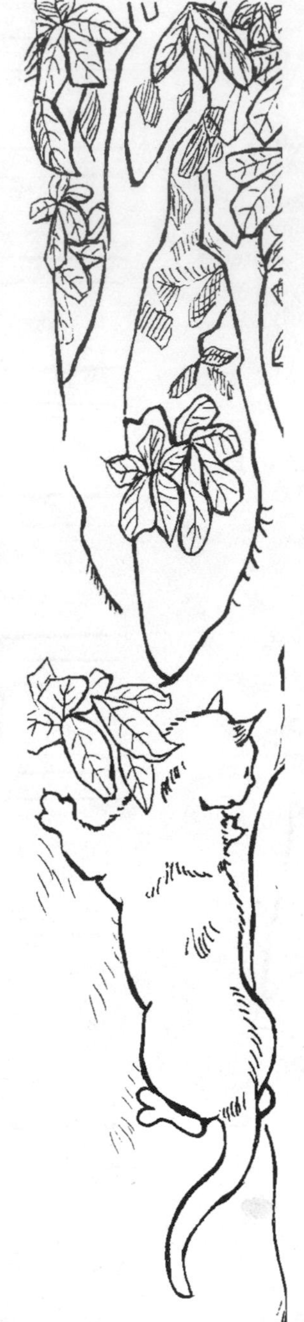

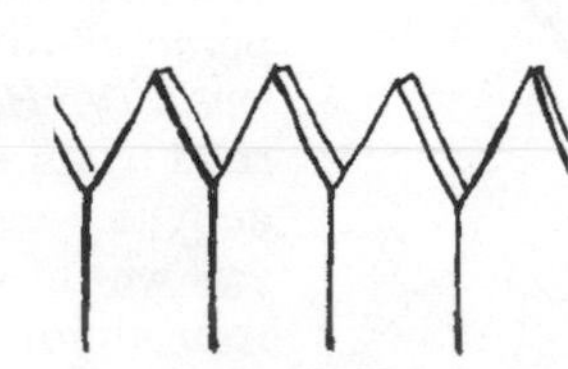

Some of the activities are more challenging than others. These include: House-Cat eyes (page 8); Cat information (pages 16–17) and the changing the tense activity in 'Creating a mood' (page 11).

Less able children may need teacher or peer support for these more challenging activities.

TIME-SCALE

This is not a long book but it is one which rewards closer reading and looking. The aim of *Read and Respond* is to slow down children's reading in order for them to think more carefully about their own responses and the way the story is put together. It is ideally suited as a focus for Literacy Hour work over a week or as part of a group reading programme using a range of the activities provided in this book.

MATCHING THE BOOK TO YOUR CLASS

This is a highly accessible book as it integrates pictures and words in an imaginative way. There is plenty for less able readers to get to grips with, but it also offers sufficient challenge for more able readers to think carefully about how Helen Cooper has crafted her book.

The House Cat should engage both boys and girls as it provides a good mix of character, action and pertinent and realistic issues.

TEACHING POTENTIAL OF *THE HOUSE CAT*

The House Cat offers learning opportunities in the following curriculum areas:

English
- writing poetry
- writing and developing arguments
- reading for information
- studying language features.

Art
- symbolism in art.

Geography
- exploring sense of place.

GLOSSARY

Always use the correct terminology when talking about books. It would be helpful if the children know the key terms listed below. Always teach and use the words in the context of an activity.

Encourage children to use these terms in their own discussion or written work:

- author/illustrator
- character
- setting
- plot
- simile
- fiction/non-fiction.

BACKGROUND KNOWLEDGE

Some activities may be more successful if you provide a model for the children to follow.

The following activities would benefit from this approach:
Cat poems (pages 6–7), House-Cat eyes (page 8), Building characters (page 9), Cat information (pages 16–17) and Writing a 'found' poem (pages 22–23).

RESOURCES

The majority of the activities in this book require the usual range of classroom equipment for reading and writing tasks only. In some activities, children are required to make drawings for which they will also need paper and pencils. Some other activities such as 'House-Cat eyes' on page 8, invite the children to develop their drawings using other art materials such as paints, brushes, pastels and crayons for the extension idea.

OTHER BOOKS BY HELEN COOPER

Helen Cooper has written and illustrated a range of books for children. These include:
The Bear Under the Stairs (Picture Corgi)
Little Monster Did it! (Picture Corgi)
Ella and the Rabbit (Frances Lincoln)
Tale of Bear (Doubleday) also *Tale of Pig*, *Frog*, *Duck*
The Baby Who Wouldn't Go to Bed (Corgi)
Kit and the Magic Kite (Picture Corgi)
Pumpkin Soup (Doubleday)

TEACHERS' NOTES

WAYS IN
PICTURE CLUES
Aims: to introduce how to look for clues about a story in pictures; to build anticipation for reading the story.
Teaching points: check that the children understand what 'endpapers' are. They need to look closely at them to make informed guesses about the setting and the main character of the story. If necessary, revise the main ingredients of stories – characters, plot, setting, events – as an introduction to the activity. Start a working chart on sugar paper to add to as they read the story. Make two columns: one headed 'Clues from the text' and the other 'Clues from the drawings' and take suggestions from this activity to start it off.
Extension: extend the chart by adding further categories such as character information, events in the story and so on, using the same column approach. Encourage children to use it to remind themselves of the story as they read.

PICTURE FLICKING
Aim: to anticipate the storyline using only five pictures from the book.
Teaching points: introduce the idea of a 'bone pattern' as a storytelling aid. This involves selecting five or seven key words or pictures, from a story and using these as the only support for telling the story. Mix up the pictures and introduce a sequencing activity prior to reading the story.
Extension: show how a 'picture flick' is a good browsing technique to get the gist of a story. Demonstrate this with a known picture book and then let the children try the technique with other picture books. What can they tell about a book from this technique?

CAT POEMS
Aims: to think carefully about how two different poets have written about the nature of cats; to think about different rhyme patterns in poems.
Teaching points: this is a challenging activity and, depending on children's previous experiences, it may need modelling. Either use one of the poems given, or use another cat poem such as 'The Tom-Cat' by Don Marquis, 'The Song of the Jellicles' by TS Eliot or 'The Singing Cat' by Stevie Smith to model the activity.
Extension: when they have read the poem, ask the children to sketch a picture to show what it makes them think of. Talk about mind pictures as a way of introducing imagery in poetry and discuss how pictures in picture books give additional information about character, mood and setting. Choose another animal poem and create an illustrated version using the children's mind pictures.

MAKING SENSE
HOUSE-CAT EYES
Aim: to introduce the idea of symbolism; to look at Helen Cooper's use of perspective and close up in her drawings.
Teaching points: introduce the activity as a whole-class discussion about Helen Cooper's use of perspective. Compare the picture of the House-Cat on the endpapers with the picture of him with the symbol in his eyes.
Extension: provide paints and pastels for the children to work up their drawings into more ambitious artwork and experiment with the art techniques used by Helen Cooper.

BUILDING CHARACTER
Aim: to explore the interrelationship between words and pictures in building up characters.
Teaching points: this activity builds on 'Picture clues' on page 4, extending from the information we can 'read' from a picture to the way pictures and words interrelate in good picture books to build characters.
Extension: children can try changing the words, pictures and colours on the Spode-Fawcett pages to make the reader more sympathetic, and the words, pictures and colours on the Jennifer pages to make the reader dislike Jennifer. You could model the Spode-Fawcett transformation perhaps, and then set pairs to work on the Jennifer transformation. Display the children's changed pages to show how different author/illustrators get their message across. Try the same activity on other picture books with which the children are familiar or with other books by the same author.

CREATING A MOOD
Aim: to consider how different verbs create different moods and the effects of changing the tense from present to past.
Teaching points: put the children into writing pairs to work on this activity. It asks children to look very closely at the function of verbs. It is important to give them time to reflect on the effects of the changes and to compare ideas.
Extension: follow up the activity by deleting other parts of speech – verbs, adjectives or adverbs – in poetry or other short extracts. Encourage children to consider how these parts of speech work and what effects they have in

writing. Sort some stories from the class library into two lists: present tense and past tense. Which list is bigger? Why is past tense more popular?

SENSES SIMILES

Aim: to consider how similes create vivid pictures in the mind.
Teaching points: introduce the activity as a whole-class shared writing context, focusing on the first two similes. Collaborative writing will demonstrate there can be as many similes as there are minds working on them! Collect suggestions on a chart and add to it as the activity progresses. The children's drawings based on the similes may be very different to Helen Cooper's originals which can lead to discussion about why this might be.
Extension: go on to introduce metaphors using a shared writing context and work through a couple of examples from the sheet such as 'He smells a horrid noisy highway screeching angrily.'

TOM-CAT'S SENSES MAP/CAT-QUICK!

Aims: to recall a section using pictures to 'map' it out; to recap the story using question and answer format.
Teaching points: discourage children from merely copying the sense map in the book but encourage them to use it for checking if necessary. The oral part of the activity is important to help fix the sequence of events in the children's minds. The second part of the sheet should then be completed from memory. Children's writing will draw on the words and the pictures in the story. Discuss the differences between their writing and Helen Cooper's story.
Extension: make a six-page 'question and answer' zigzag picture book with questions in the top half and answers in words and/or pictures in the bottom half of each page.

DEVELOPING IDEAS

ANIMAL INSTINCT

Aims: to explore use of the senses as an alternative way of mapping a familiar route; to recap this section of the story.
Teaching points: depending on the level of your children's experience, you could model a familiar journey with children in school, for example the way from your classroom to the dinner hall. Children can then attempt the activity for themselves, writing or drawing their own sensemaps.
Extension: children could write sense maps for a pet. Ask them to imagine their dog/cat followed them to school and had to find its way home unaided.

CAT INFORMATION

Aim: to explore how we read to find out information, especially using headings.
Teaching points: introduce the activity by discussing some differences between fiction and non-fiction. Sort through a mixed pile of books and prompt children to generate criteria for recognizing the two genres. This will help them to complete the first part of the activity – what they expect to find in an information book. Talk about terms such as fiction, non-fiction, layout, headings. Discuss why headings are useful. For the second page, read the information sections aloud to familiarize the children before they try the activity. Depending on level of ability, model the activity using a page from a different information book.
Extension: repeat the activity using another non-fiction book, deleting headings and asking children to come up with suitable headings as a way of identifying the key idea in each section.

WHERE SHOULD TOM-CAT LIVE?

Aims: to formulate two sides of an argument and come to conclusions about an issue; to develop a structured argument using planner and writing frame.
Teaching points: it is important that children find evidence from the story, but also that they empathize with the people involved on the two sides of the argument. Model and demonstrate use of the planner and the frame using a different theme if children are unfamiliar with the approach. Present finished writing as a

class display, labelling stages of the writing process and framework to make the 'writing journey' clear.
Extension: list other issues of concern to the children, such as: Should you wear school uniform? Is it right or wrong to have homework? Then, over time, examine the different points of view. Compare a different type of non-fiction writing, such as report writing. Work on the frameworks and features of other types of non-fiction writing.

WHAT MAKES A HOME?

Aims: to explore connotations of the word 'home'; to introduce the 'stepping stone' technique for mind-mapping or brainstorming initial ideas; to work collaboratively on a poem.
Teaching points: progress from individual work based on response to the book, to pairs working on the stepping stones, then small groups collaboratively working on a poem. You can then orchestrate the different stages of activity, pooling ideas and modelling at each stage. At the stage of developing the sentences, introduce oral drafting and redrafting. At the collaborative poem writing stage, write up children's sentences and physically demonstrate how ideas can be moved about and shaped to make best sense.
Extension: encourage the children to illustrate their poems and make a display of them. Make up 'Home is...' stepping stones and poems for Jennifer or the Spode-Fawcetts, based on the children's reading of *The House Cat*.

WRITING A 'FOUND' POEM

Aims: to introduce the cinquain form; to select most effective vocabulary from a short piece of text and work it into a cinquain.
Teaching points: this is a challenging activity and would benefit from being worked through with the group or class. You could use a modified cinquain with the same pattern but using words rather than syllables, for example 2 words, 4 words, 6 words, 8 words, 2 words. Using words from the text makes children concentrate on the meaning and the pattern without having to create vocabulary too. Encourage them to use additional words and to modify the text, if needed, for sense.

CAT WORDS

Aim: to focus on invented language in the text and invent new vocabulary.
Teaching points: encourage children to use their own knowledge first, before they try a dictionary to find other cat words.
Extension: compile a cat words glossary or cat words mini dictionary of your own.

CHARACTER PROFILE

Aim: to assess understanding and empathy with one of the main characters.
Teaching points: remind children that they will find information from the pictures as well as the text. Ensure they understand that for some parts of the sheet they won't always find specific information on their character in the book, but will need to use their own ideas, based on what they know from the story.

EVALUATION
A REVIEW OF *THE HOUSE CAT*

Aim: to come to conclusions about the story and write a review for the back cover.
Teaching points: the first part could be worked through with class or group. Encourage children to speculate about why the publisher printed the quote on the back cover of the book. Provide a simpler frame if the *Books for Keeps* layout is too difficult such as:
The House Cat by Helen Cooper is a ____________ book. The sort of people I think would enjoy it are ____________. Helen Cooper's pictures are ____________.